The Concise Illustrated Book of
Whales and Dolphins

Ray Gambell

Brian Trodd Publishing House Limited

Published in 1991 by
Brian Trodd Publishing House Limited
27 Swinton Street, London WC1X 9NW

ISBN 1 85361 194 8

Printed in Portugal

Front cover: Humpback Whale and calf
Title page: Bottlenose Dolphin
Right: Killer Whale
Back cover: Bottlenose Dolphin

Photographic Acknowledgements

All photographs supplied by EarthViews Photo
Library and the following photographers:
Kenneth C. Balcomb III, 4, 10; Peter Folkiens,
Back cover, 20; Jeff Jacobsen, 6, 34; Thomas
Johnson, 7, 11; Stephen Leatherwood, 8; Stan
Minasian, 22; Robert Pitman, title page, 23, 25,
27, 29, 30, 38, 39, 41, 46; Keith Rittmaster, 24;
Richard Sears, 9, 31, 45; Gregory Silber, 36; Ted
Stephenson, 18, 43; James D. Watt, Front cover,
12, 15, 26, 35, 37, 40; Marc Webber, 28, 42;
Gordon Williamson, 15; Birgit Winning, 14; John
Woestendiel, 17; Keith Rittmaster and Victoria
Thayer, 16; Bernie Tershey and Craig Strong, 13.

All artworks by David More/Linden Artists

CONTENTS

INTRODUCTION

The whales, dolphins and porpoises make up the order Cetacea. There are three sub-orders: the **Archaeoceti** or 'ancient whales', all extinct and known only from fossils; the **Mysticeti** or 'moustached whales', which include the modern baleen or whalebone whales; and the **Odontoceti**, which are the living toothed whales, dolphins and porpoises.

In this book more than 40 representative members of the Cetacea are described and illustrated to demonstrate the various features of these fascinating creatures. They are all air-breathing, warm-blooded mammals that give birth to one calf at a time, which feeds on its mother's milk for some months after birth.

The baleen whales (**Mysticetes**) have horny baleen plates growing down from the upper jaws but no teeth in the mouth. They are primarily filter feeders, which strain small planktonic food and fish mainly from the surface layers of the ocean. They carry out annual migrations between the warm water breeding grounds occupied in winter and the high latitude feeding areas frequented in summer. Baleen whales have paired blowholes on the top of the head. They include three main families:

The **Balaenidae** are the right whales. These whales have long, fine baleen, but no dorsal fin or throat grooves.

The **Balaenopteridae** or rorquals have a number of longitudinal throat grooves which allow the mouth to expand greatly to hold large quantities of water and food organisms before they are filtered out through the short baleen plates.

The **Eschrichtiidae** is the family of the gray whale. This has short coarse baleen and only two to five deep throat grooves.

The toothed Cetacea (**Odontocetes**) have teeth but no baleen plates in the mouth. They actively hunt for fish and squid as their main food, and many carry out seasonal migrations related to the movements and abundance of the prey. They have a single blowhole, and include a number of different families:

The **Physeteridae** includes the largest of the toothed whales, the sperm whale with its very large head compared to the body.

The **Monodontidae** contains two species, the narwhal and the beluga or white whale, which have blunt heads and no dorsal fin on the white or pale bodies.

The **Ziphiidae** are the beaked whales. They have a dorsal fin set well back on the long body, and small flippers.

The **Delphinidae** are the oceanic dolphins. This is a big family with many species. All have fairly large curved dorsal fins.

The **Phocoenidae** or true porpoises have a short beak, and a small triangular dorsal fin (if present) on a small body. The teeth are spatulate or spade-shaped.

The **Platanistidae** are the river dolphins. They live in fresh water, have long beaks, and are generally light in colour.

Killer Whale

BLUE WHALE

Balaenoptera musculus

Family: Balaenopteridae
Distribution: Found in all oceans of the world, mainly in the deeper waters off continental shelves and ice edges. A pygmy sub-species has been identified in the southern Indian Ocean
Length: 30.5m (100 ft) in the Southern Hemisphere, 26m (85 ft) in the Northern Hemisphere, females larger than males
Description: The body is huge, but long and streamlined. It is mottled bluish-grey with lighter spots on the back and sides. The head is broad and U-shaped when viewed from above, and flattened in front of the blowholes. A very small dorsal fin is set well back towards the tail.

General remarks: This is the largest animal that has ever lived. Blue whales are usually seen singly or in pairs, but larger concentrations may occur in the polar feeding areas. The main food is shrimp-like crustaceans (krill) engulfed and filtered from the top 100m of the sea through their coarse baleen bristles. When swimming fast, the head and blow holes disappear before the back and dorsal fin break the surface, giving a 'wheeling' appearance.

The slender vertical blow can reach as high as 9m (30 ft) after dives lasting 10–20 minutes. Females give birth to a single calf every two or three years in the warm water breeding grounds after a pregnancy which lasts nearly 12 months. The calf is 7m (23 ft) long and weighs 2.5 tons at birth. It grows to 15m (50 ft) and weighs 23 tons by the time it is weaned seven months later on the high latitude feeding grounds.

BOWHEAD WHALE

Balaena mysticetus

Family: Balaenidae
Distribution: Circumpolar in the Arctic, divided into five separate stocks
Length: Females up to 18.5m (61 ft), the males slightly smaller
Description: The enormous head of this thick-set animal makes up a third of its total length. The large mouth houses the longest baleen plates of any whale, which can measure up to 4m (13 ft). The lower jaw is strongly bowed, with a white chin patch. The rest of the body is all black. The top of the head, the rostrum, is smooth, arched and very narrow, and it is enfolded at the sides by the lower lips. There is no fin on the back.

General remarks: The migrations of bowhead whales seem to be governed by the movements of the Arctic ice. The whales winter near the southern limits of the pack-ice, then move northwards as the ice retreats in summer to feed on copepods, euphausids and other small plankton. They skim the food organisms at the surface through their fine baleen fringes, but they may also feed near the bottom in shallow areas. Bowheads are slow swimmers, usually travelling singly or in small groups, and they can stay submerged for up to 40 minutes. This enables them to move under the ice from one breathing hole to another. The blow is distinctively V-shaped from the widely spaced blowholes. Females probably calve at intervals of two years or more, after a pregnancy lasting about 13 months. Most births occur in spring or early summer and the newborn calf is 4-4.5m (13-15 ft) long.

BRYDE'S WHALE

Balaenoptera edeni

Family: Balaenopteridae
Distribution: Tropical and warm temperate waters around the world. A smaller coastal form has been identified off South Africa, Brazil, California and Japan in addition to an offshore form
Length: 14m (46 ft) for the offshore form, slightly smaller for the coastal form
Description: The dark grey body, paler below, is very similar to the sei whale's, with which it has been long confused. The chief distinguishing feature is the presence of three prominent ridges on the head of the Bryde's whale in front of the blowholes, one on either side of the usual central ridge.

General remarks: The main food of the Bryde's whale is schooling fish, such as pilchards, anchovies, herring and mackerel, together with planktonic crustacea. When feeding, they often turn on to their sides. The baleen plates of the offshore form are longer and broader than those of the coastal form and more similar to the sei whale. They are reported to approach ships through curiosity, and are usually seen singly or in pairs. Deeper divers than sei whales, they come to the surface at a steep angle to breathe. Coastal populations appear to breed throughout the year, but the offshore form mate and calve chiefly in the autumn, with births occurring every second year. Some tropical populations are permanently resident, but those in temperate waters may undertake regular north-south seasonal migrations. Like all rorquals, the females grow larger than the males.

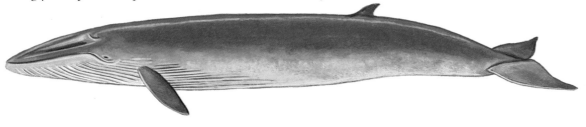

FIN WHALE

Balaenoptera physalus

Family: Balaenopteridae
Distribution: All oceans worldwide, particularly over deep water
Length: 27m (88 ft) in the Southern Hemisphere, 24m (79 ft) in the Northern Hemisphere, males smaller than females
Description: The head is V-shaped and the slender streamlined body has a sharp ridge along the spine. The prominent dorsal fin is set about a third of the body length from the tail. The colour is dark grey-brown on the back and sides, often with a pale chevron just behind the head, and white below. The colouring on the head is asymmetrical, with the right side of the lower jaw white and the left dark.

General remarks: Fin whales dive to at least 230m (755 ft). They rise obliquely to the surface after a deep dive, arching the back high in the air before diving again. Dives usually last for 6-7 minutes, but they can extend this time to 15 minutes. The blow on surfacing is an elongated inverted cone up to 6m (20 ft) tall. Fin whales often travel in groups of 6-7 individuals, but they may also be found singly or in pairs. They feed on krill and other pelagic crustacea, particularly in the Antarctic, but a wide variety of fish such as herring, capelin and cod are consumed by gulping in the higher latitudes of the Northern Hemisphere. Fin whales mate in the warmer waters of each hemisphere in winter and then migrate to the polar feeding grounds in summer. The single calf is 6.4m (21 ft) long at birth and weighs 1.9 tons after a pregnancy lasting just under a year. It is weaned 6-8 months later.

GRAY WHALE

Eschrichtius robustus

Family: Eschrichtiidae
Distribution: North Pacific Ocean, with the main stock along the coast of North America and a small Asian stock
Length: 14m (46 ft), males a little smaller
Description: The mottled grey body appears spindle-shaped, with a narrow pointed head and slim tail stock. The head slopes downwards from the blowholes when viewed from the side, and the mouth appears slightly arched. There is no dorsal fin as such, but rather a low hump two-thirds of the way back followed by a series of knobs towards the tail. Barnacles encrust the skin of the Gray Whale, providing shelter for cyamid whale lice.

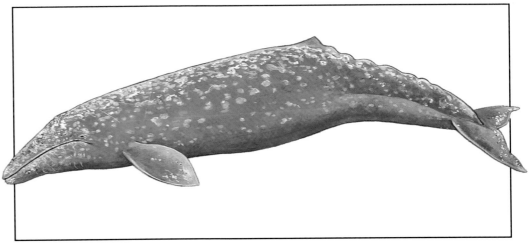

General remarks: The North American population winters in the breeding lagoons of Baja California, Mexico, and spends the summer feeding in the Bering, Chukchi and Beaufort Seas in the Arctic. The round trip of 10,000km (6,000 miles) is the longest annual migration known. The whales swim close to shore at an average speed of 6-7km/h (4 mph) when southbound but only 3km/h (2 mph) northbound when the newborn calves are with their mothers. Amphipods and other invertebrates are grubbed up from the muddy bottom for food, and this behaviour wears down the baleen plates more on the right side than the left. Nursing females try to stay apart from the other whales in the breeding lagoons, where the whales are often very active 'spy hopping' (standing vertically with the head held above the water) or 'lobtailing' (splashing the tail down hard on the surface).

HUMPBACK WHALE

Megaptera novaengliae

Family: Balaenopteridae
Distribution: Worldwide, from the polar seas to tropical islands and coastlines
Length: Females 16m (53 ft), males 15m (49 ft)
Description: The robust grey-black body narrows rapidly towards the tail, and there is some white on the throat and belly regions. The head is broad and rounded seen from above, and there are many prominent fleshy knobs, often with conspicuous barnacles and less noticeable cyamid whale lice. The white flippers are very long, up to one-third of the body length.

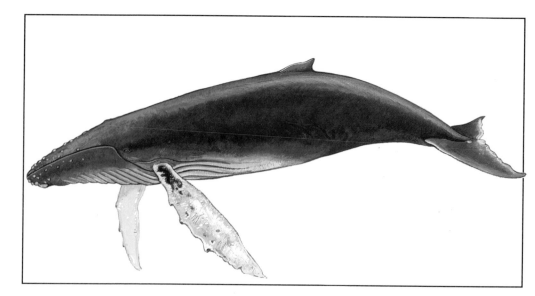

General remarks: The main food items taken are krill and schooling fish, which may be concentrated from below by a bubble curtain produced in a stream from the blowhole of the circling whale before it lunges up open-mouthed to engulf the prey. Humpbacks often leap clear of the water, slap the surface with a flipper, or 'lobtail'. The tail is often thrown high before a dive, exposing the variable colour pattern of the underside by which the whales can be individually recognized. Groups of up to a dozen humpbacks may congregate close inshore on the tropical winter breeding grounds and the summer polar feeding grounds, but 1-3 whales are common at mating, made up of a female, her calf and an attendant male. The males vocalize in extended songs lasting for up to half an hour during the breeding season.

MINKE WHALE

Balaenoptera acutorostrata

Family: Balaenopteridae
Distribution: All oceans from the ice-edge to temperate and tropical waters
Length: 11m (36 ft) in the Northern Hemisphere, 9m (30 ft) in the Southern Hemisphere, males smaller than females
Description: The body is a sleek and slender dark grey-black, with white belly and paler chevron markings behind the head and extending down the flanks. Minke whales in the Northern Hemisphere have a white band across the flippers. The head is narrowly pointed, and there is a tall curved dorsal fin set about two-thirds of the way back from the tip of the snout.

General remarks: The smallest of the rorquals, the minke whale is frequently found singly, in pairs or threes, with larger concentrations in feeding areas. They feed on krill in the Southern Hemisphere, and also schooling fish such as herring, cod and capelin in the Northern Hemisphere. They may segregate by age or sexual condition, so that many pregnant or lactating females can be found together. Pregnancy lasts 10-11 months and the new-born calf is 2.6m (8.5 ft) long. Females can give birth every 1-2 years. Some minke whales are permanent residents while others undertake lengthy migrations. They can be found close to shore and will also approach stationary boats. In loose pack-ice, minke whales may 'spy hop' – poke their heads vertically through the ice – to breathe. They can also leap clear of the water, re-entering either smoothly head first or with a great splash.

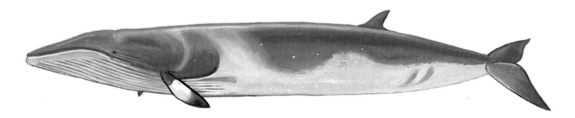

RIGHT WHALES

Eubalaena glacialis, Eubalaena australis

Family: Balaenidae
Distribution: The northern and southern right whales are found in the cooler waters of the two hemispheres, isolated from each other by the warm tropics
Length: 17m (56 ft), the males smaller
Description: The rotund body is black with a few irregular white patches on the belly. There is no dorsal fin, and the large head, which makes up a quarter of the total body length, is marked by a series of callosities or growths. Their positions vary from whale to whale, allowing the animals to be individually recognized. They also provide shelter for cyamid whale lice.

General remarks: The externally similar northern and southern right whales may be one, two or even three species if the North Atlantic and North Pacific populations prove to be different. Pregnancy lasts for one year, and it is 1-2 years before weaning occurs; the females therefore give birth every three years on average. They do not return to the breeding areas in the intervening years although the males usually return annually. Right whales congregate in coastal waters to calve and mate in winter, and move to higher latitudes in summer to feed on copepods and other small plankton which they strain through their very fine baleen bristles. Although slow swimmers they can be surprisingly acrobatic, breaching out of the water, and slapping the surface with their flippers and tail flukes. The distinctive V-shaped blow reaches to 5m (16 ft).

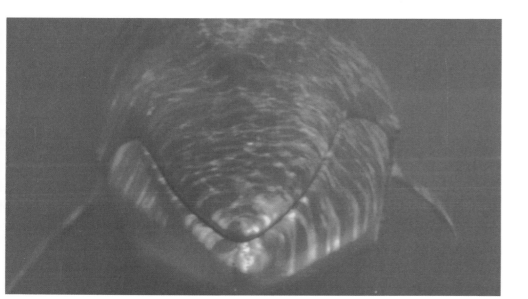

SEI WHALE

Balaenoptera borealis

Family: Balaenopteridae
Distribution: Temperate and oceanic waters worldwide, but not venturing very far into the polar seas
Length: 21m (69 ft) in the Southern Hemisphere, 19m (62 ft) in the Northern Hemisphere, males a little smaller
Description: The sleek body is a steely-grey colour on the back and sides, often appearing galvanized because of the number of scars from fish bites. There is some white on the belly but the undersides of the flukes and flippers are dark. The head seems slightly arched when seen from the side, and the dorsal fin is large and erect.

General remarks: Sei whales feed by skimming with open mouths at the surface of the water. The fine bristles fringing their baleen plates trap small copepods and other plankton, while small fish and squid also form an important part of the diet. They are fast swimmers, and can reach speeds of 40km/h (25 mph). They do not dive very deeply and are normally found in groups of 2-5 animals. The blow is an inverted cone no more than 4.5m (15 ft) high, and the diving pattern tends to be very regular. The seasonal movements of sei whales are considered unpredictable, but although they do not go far towards the poles, they do carry out regular annual migrations between the higher and lower latitudes. The females give birth every 2-3 years in the winter months after a pregnancy lasting 12 months. The calf is 4.5m (15 ft) long at birth and in 6-7 months grows to 8.5m (28 ft) before it is weaned.

SPERM WHALE

Physeter catodon

Family: Physeteridae
Distribution: All oceans, from the equator to the polar seas
Length: Males up to 18m (59 ft), females no greater than 12m (39 ft)
Description: The blunt head makes up to a quarter or a third of the total length. It is relatively larger in males than females. A single blowhole is set far forward on the left of the snout. The body is dark brownish-grey, corrugated behind the head, with white or pale patches on the belly. A low dorsal hump is followed by a series of bumps towards the tail. Two rows of up to 25 conical teeth protrude from the narrow underslung lower jaw.

General remarks: Sperm whales have a complex social organization and can be found in aggregations of up to 50 or more. The core unit is the group of 10-15 females with their calves and immature males. Large solitary bulls join them in the breeding season, and bachelor males form smaller groups as they mature. The largest old males venture into the polar seas; the females and younger males range only as far as 40° latitude in the spring and summer from the equatorial zone occupied in the winter months. They feed mainly on deep-living squid and fish. Large males routinely dive for 60 minutes or more and have been recorded down to 3,000m (10,000 ft). The blow on surfacing is projected obliquely forwards. Pregnancy extends over 15 months, and the 1-ton calf is born at a length of 4m (13 ft). Suckling continues for several years with a calving interval of 4-5 years.

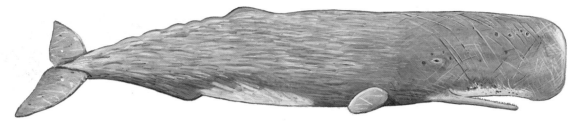

Berardius bairdii, Berardius arnuxii

Baird's Beaked Whale

Family: Ziphiidae

Distribution: Baird's beaked whale is found in the North Pacific Ocean, Arnoux's in the Southern Hemisphere

Length: Baird's beaked whale up to 13m (42 ft); Arnoux's beaked whale 9m (30 ft)

Description: The long beak has two triangular teeth at the tip of the lower jaw. There is a bulbous forehead and a crescent-shaped blowhole on the top of the head. The body is rotund, with a small triangular dorsal fin. The colour is grey-brown to black, with white patches below. Circular white scars and tooth scratches are common on the body.

General remarks: It is uncertain whether these whales are the same or are two different species. They are geographically separated in their two hemispheres and the northern form grows rather larger than that in the south. Arnoux's beaked whales have been seen in the cooler waters of the Southern Hemisphere but few have been examined. Baird's beaked whales are confined to waters far offshore and deeper than 1,000m (3,300 ft) in the North Pacific. There is evidence for a marked segregation of the males and females, and the females also grow rather larger than the males. The populations migrate northwards in summer and southwards in winter and form groups of 2-20 or occasionally 30 animals which move and blow together. The blow is low and indistinct, and they have been timed to dive for more than 40 minutes. Their main food items are squid, octopus and deep sea fish.

Arnoux's Beaked Whale

BELUGA or WHITE WHALE

Delphinapterus leucas

Family: Monodontidae
Distribution: Shallow coastal areas of the Arctic and sub-Arctic
Length: 4.5m (15 ft)
Description: The tapered, robust body has surface creases and folds of fat, but no dorsal fin or hump. The head is small with a prominent forehead (or 'melon') over-hanging a short beak. Unusually for whales, the neck is well defined and flexible so that the head is quite mobile. The blowhole is a transverse slit just in front of the neck crease. Newborn animals are slate grey-brown, becoming bluish grey before the pure white adult colouring develops.

General remarks: Some populations of white whales carry out extensive seasonal migrations while others remain in one area all year round. Although well adapted to live in the cold water amongst the ice floes, large groups numbering hundreds or thousands of whales congregate in the warm Arctic rivers, estuaries and shallow coastal bays during the summer months. The calves are born at this time at a length of 1.6m (5 ft) after a pregnancy lasting 14½ months. They remain with their mothers for two years. A wide range of food is taken by the adults, including fish, crustaceans and squid. Belugas produce a variety of sounds underwater, and these whistles and squeals are often clearly audible above the surface or through the hull of a boat, giving rise to the name 'sea canary'. The melon is quite plastic in form and changes shape as these sounds are made.

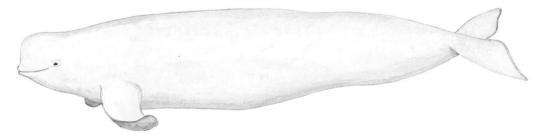

BLAINVILLE'S BEAKED WHALE

Mesoplodon densirostris

Family: Ziphiidae

Distribution: Found in tropical and warm temperate waters around the world

Length: 4.6m (15 ft)

Description: A pair of massive teeth is set in the middle of each side of the lower jaw. The teeth are flattened from side to side and in adult males grow up to 15-20cm (6-in) in length and 7.5cm (3 in) in width. The body is spindle-shaped and has a small curved dorsal fin. It tapers from the sturdy centre section to a small head with a long prominent beak. The colour is black or dark grey above and paler below. There are blotchy markings as well as extensive scratches and scars.

General remarks: This is probably the most widely distributed of the Mesoplodons, with records of strandings coming from the warm waters on either side of the equator in the Atlantic, Indian and Pacific Oceans. Groups of 5-12 animals have been observed swimming together off Hawaii. They appear to be shy and make only indistinct blows, so that they are not easy to detect or follow. When they surface to breathe the head breaks the surface first, pointing upwards, and then slaps down on the surface rather awkwardly before the body rolls over without showing the tail. They are slow swimming whales and can dive for 20 minutes or longer. Their diet includes squid, which they probably catch on the deep dives. The most striking feature of this whale is the teeth, which become more pronounced in older animals, appearing to be tipped slightly forwards and usually encrusted with barnacles.

BOTTLENOSE DOLPHIN

Tursiops truncatus

Family: Delphinidae
Distribution: Present around the world except in the coldest waters
Length: 4m (13 ft), females smaller
Description: The sturdy body is dark grey above and paler below, but there are many variations in the shade and extent of the colour pattern in different populations. Complex markings and lines occur particularly around the head. The clearly-defined beak is relatively short and thick. The 20-26 pointed teeth in each side of the upper jaw and 18-24 each side of the lower jaw wear down in older animals. The dorsal fin is high and curved, set in the centre of the back.

General remarks: There appear to be distinct inshore and off-shore populations of these dolphins in most parts of the world. The coastal form occurs in groups of 10-50 animals, but several hundreds of the offshore form may be found together. They take a wide variety of food organisms, including fish, squid and crustacea, probably on an opportunistic basis. Mating and calving activity is most common in spring and autumn. Pregnancy lasts a year and the mother suckles her single calf for 12-18 months. In the wild, bottlenose dolphins are very active animals, riding the bow waves of ships as well as ocean waves, and those that live near shore will also surf in the breakers. They can leap 4.5-6m (15-20 ft) clear of the surface of the water, and this behaviour is often utilized in presenting these dolphins when they are held in captivity for display.

BOTTLENOSE WHALES

Hyperoodon ampullatus, H. planifrons

Family: Ziphiidae

Distribution: The northern species (*H. ampullatus*) is found in the northern North Atlantic, the southern (*H. planifrons*) in the southern Hemisphere

Length: Northern bottlenose males 9.8m (33 ft), females 8m (26 ft). The southern bottlenose whales are rather smaller

Description: The head has a dolphin-like beak and a bulbous forehead. The rounded body with a curved dorsal fin is brown-grey, becoming lighter on the sides and belly with age. The large males have a white head, and a pair of conical teeth erupt at the tip of their lower jaw. There are usually extensive scratches and scars on the older animals.

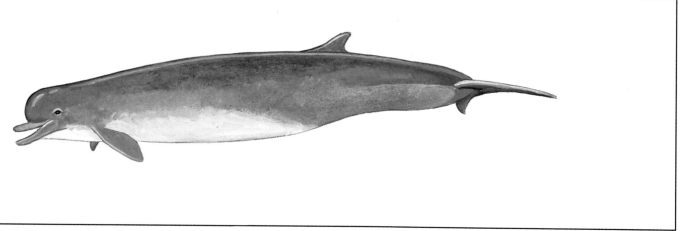

General remarks: Normally found in cold, deep water, bottlenose whales have a reputation for being deep divers and can stay submerged for over an hour. The southern species is only poorly known from a few strandings and sightings. Northern bottlenose whales will approach boats as if through curiosity, and they appear to have strong social ties, forming tight-knit groups of up to 10 individuals. They exhibit strong care-giving behaviour and tend to stay with wounded companions. They feed on squid and also pelagic fish such as herring. There is some segregation of the sexes as the whales move from the lower latitudes of the North Atlantic which they occupy in the winter months. Breeding reaches a peak in spring with a 12 months-long pregnancy. After spending the summer in subarctic and arctic waters the whales drift south again as the ice advances.

BOUTU

Inia geoffrensis

Family: Platinistidae
Distribution: Restricted to the Amazo
and Orinoco rivers of South America
Length: 3m (10 ft)
Description: The body is thick-set, wit
a long, low dorsal hump rather than a fin
and long flexible flippers. It is grey abov
and paler below, the colour becomin
lighter in older animals and suffused wit
pink particularly on the underside. Th
head can move through a wide angle an
has a long tube-like whiskered beak an
prominent rounded forehead. The 24-3
teeth in each half of the jaws are a simpl
conical shape in the front of the mouth bu
more like molars towards the back.

General remarks: The boutu or Amazon river dolphin is usually found singly or in pairs, but it may form larger groups when the water level in the river is lower. They feed on fish near the bottom, which are caught with the pointed teeth at the front of the mouth and then crushed by the rear teeth. Although these animals can see with their reduced eyes, sometimes putting their heads above the surface to look around, they probably rely mainly on the sensory bristles on the beak and on echo location to navigate and to find their prey in the muddy water conditions in which they live. They are slow-moving animals, generally swimming into the current at 1.6-3.2km/h (1-2 mph), but they are capable of making a burst of 12-16km/h (7.5-10 mph) and can leap clear of the surface. Pregnancy lasts for a little over 10 months, and the single calf is born at a length of around 75cm (2.5 ft).

BURMEISTER'S PORPOISE

Phocoena spinipinnis

Family: Phocoenidae
Distribution: Found in the shallow coastal waters of South America
Length: 1.8m (6 ft)
Description: This all black porpoise has a distinctive dorsal fin. It is set at a very low angle behind the mid-point of the back, and the trailing edge both curves and points backwards. The Latin specific name, *spinipinnis*, refers to the three rows of flattened spines or protuberances which almost always occur on the leading edge of the dorsal fin and sometimes on the edges of the tapering flippers. There are 14–16 teeth in each half of the upper jaw and 17–19 in the lower.

General remarks: Small groups numbering 2–8 of these porpoises are found in the temperate inshore waters of South America. They occur from Uruguay on the east coast and Peru on the west coast southwards along the continent, and they are also known from strandings on the beaches and shores of Tierra del Fuego as well as from reports around the Falkland Islands. They are rather shy and unobtrusive animals, rarely jumping or showing much of themselves at the surface. Nevertheless they are well known to the fishermen particularly of Chile and Peru, who catch them directly for food and bait. Unfortunately, large numbers are also taken accidentally in fishing nets set for fin fish as well. The porpoises are known to feed on fish and squid.

COMMERSON'S DOLPHIN

Cephalorhynchus commersonii

Family: Delphinidae
Distribution: Found in the coastal waters of the western South Atlantic and southern Indian Ocean
Length: 1.7m (5.5 ft)
Description: The chunky body is boldly coloured. The head and the area of the back extending from the dorsal fin to the tail are black, while the rest of the body is white, including a white patch on the throat. The dorsal fin is rounded with a concave trailing edge, and the flippers are also round-tipped. There are 29-30 small pointed teeth in each row of the upper and lower jaws. The mouth slopes up towards the eyes, and there is no beak.

General remarks: This uniquely coloured dolphin occurs only in the inshore waters of southern Argentina and Chile, around the Falkland Islands and South Georgia in the South Atlantic, and off Kerguelen Island in the southern Indian Ocean. Groups of 2-12 animals commonly swim together, travelling at 12km/h (7.5 mph). They leap clear of the surface of the water very frequently, often in unison. The main food items in their diet are fish, squid and krill. In the southern regions of Argentina they can be seen in the shallow waters of harbours and beaches, and in kelp beds apparently feeding. Calving activity probably reaches a peak in the summer months off Tierra del Fuego. The calves are reported to be brown in colour and the sharply demarcated zones of the adult develop with age, after passing through a black and grey phase.

COMMON DOLPHIN

Delphinus delphis

Family: Delphinidae
Distribution: Found in warm temperate and tropical seas throughout the world
Length: 2.5m (8 ft), females smaller
Description: This slender, streamlined dolphin with a tall, curved dorsal fin has a crisscross colour pattern on the sides. The black or grey-brown on the back dips down and meets the creamy white of the underside to give the flanks an hourglass effect, yellowish-white in front and grey towards the tail. A dark stripe runs from the lower jaw to the flipper, and another from the eye to the mouth. The beak is long and slender, with 40-55 sharply pointed teeth in each half of the jaws.

General remarks: This is the original dolphin from the time of the ancient Greeks. It is attracted to ships and will ride the bow wave for long periods, a habit probably originally learned from travelling with large baleen whales. It is a very gregarious species, forming herds numbering from a few dozen to several hundred animals. They feed on fish both at the surface and at depths down to 280m (910 ft), and the diet includes anchovies, lantern fish and hake, as well as squid. Calves are born chiefly in spring and autumn, at least in the eastern North Pacific. Pregnancy lasts for 10-11 months and the newborn animal is 80cm (2.5 ft) long. Pregnant and lactating females tend to segregate themselves from the other dolphins. There are no clear migrations, but some seasonal shifts of the populations occur.

CUVIER'S BEAKED WHALE

Ziphius cavirostris

Family: Ziphiidae
Distribution: Widely distributed in all oceans except the polar seas
Length: 7m (23 ft)
Description: The head is small, the forehead sloping down to a poorly defined beak. The line of the mouth turns up towards the back, and in adult males a pair of conical teeth erupts from the tip of the lower jaw and can be seen even when the mouth is closed. The rotund body, with a tall, curved dorsal fin, varies from brown to fawn or grey. The belly is lighter, with oval white blotches extending to the flanks. Tooth scratches are common on the back and sides.

General remarks: This species seems to be wary of boats and so it is not often observed at sea. Groups of generally 3-10 animals have been sighted together. Although breaching has been seen, it is probably not a common behaviour. However, stranded individuals occur widely around the world throughout the tropical and temperate zones. They are probably deep divers and can stay submerged for 30 minutes. Their main food items are squid and deepwater fish. The relatively wide blowhole is located well forward on the head, so that the blow coming from it is directed forwards and is broad and short but inconspicuous even after a long deep dive. The head becomes almost completely white in old males, and the raking scratches on the skin are evidence of fighting between these animals with their exposed teeth.

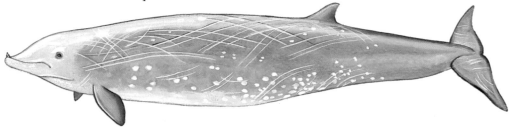

DALL'S PORPOISE

Phocoenoides dalli

Family: Phocoenidae
Distribution: The temperate and cold waters of the northern North Pacific
Length: 2.2m (7 ft)
Description: The body is chunky in build, black with a clearly defined white patch on the belly extending up the sides. The dorsal fin is short and triangular, and has a variable area of white on its rear edge, as do the relatively broad tail flukes. There is often a pronounced keel to the tail stock. The flippers are small and pointed, located well forward towards the head. The head itself is small, and there are 19-28 teeth in each side of the upper and lower jaws.

General remarks: This is a very active and fast swimming porpoise. When it charges to the surface it throws up a splash of spray called a 'rooster tail' from the appearance of the cone of water coming from the head. Groups numbering up to 20 animals usually swim together, although much larger aggregations of at least 200 porpoises have been seen. They occur in near-shore waters as well as the open sea, and will ride the bow and stern waves of ships. They often associate with Pacific white-sided dolphins and pilot whales. The single calves are born in the summer months at a length of 85-100cm (2.4-3.3 ft) after a pregnancy lasting just under a year. They suckle for a further two years and the females probably give birth every three years on average. Their main foods are squid and schooling fish such as herring, mackerel and capelin.

DUSKY DOLPHIN

Lagenorhynchus obscurus

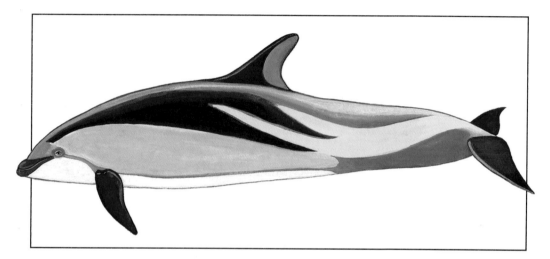

Family: Delphinidae
Distribution: Found in inshore waters all around the temperate zone of the Southern Hemisphere
Length: 2.1m (7 ft)
Description: The colour pattern on the body is complex and individually variable. The back, tail and snout are bluish-grey, shading to grey on the flanks. The overlay of these colours produces grey and black bands towards the rear of the body. The tall, slightly hooked dorsal fin is two-tone bluish-black and grey. The belly and throat are white. The snout is small, and there are 24–36 small teeth in each half of the upper and lower jaws.

General remarks: This is an acrobatic species which can bring the surface of the sea to a froth as the animals leap and somersault. Groups of 6-20 are common, but several hundred may occur together, particularly when they are feeding. Their chief food items are fish such as anchovies, and squid. When feeding, the dolphins can reach speeds of up to 14km/h (9 mph). They seem to herd the prey by their surface activity and fast splashless jumps as they follow the fish schools in hot pursuit. These dolphins are known to dive to at least 150m (490 ft) in New Zealand waters, but they are generally surface-dwelling animals which submerge normally for only a few seconds except when chasing food. Calves are born in summer off Argentina, but in mid-winter off New Zealand. Pregnancy extends over 10-11 months, and the mother nurses her single calf for 18 months.

Family: Delphinidae

Distribution: Found in offshore warm temperate and tropical waters around the world

Length: 5.5m (18 ft), females smaller

Description: The long slender body is all black except for a patch of grey on the chest between the flippers. These are placed rather far forward and have a distinctive hump on their front edge. The head tapers smoothly and overhangs the lower jaw so that the mouth appears to curve upwards. There are 8–11 large teeth in each half of the jaws. The dorsal fin is tall and curved, set midway or a little more along the back.

General remarks: These are highly gregarious and social animals, forming groups which may number from 2-50 and sometimes several hundred whales of all ages and sexual classes mixed together. They also associate with other cetacean species such as bottlenose dolphins. They will approach ships and ride the bow wave, and can swim at 24km/h (15 mph). They also ride in ocean swells and can perform high leaps clear of the water. No obvious seasonal migrations have been observed in the populations of these whales and the calves are born at all times of the year. Their chief food items are squid and large pelagic fish such as tuna. They will take fish caught on the lines of fishermen, and have also been seen eating dolphins released from seine nets. Although mainly oceanic in their distribution, large herds of false killer whales sometimes mass-strand alive on beaches.

FRASER'S DOLPHIN

Lagenodelphis hosei

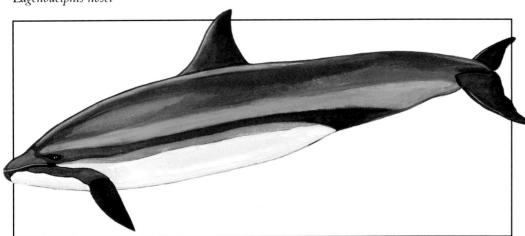

Family: Delphinidae
Distribution: Found in the warm temperate and tropical waters of the Atlantic, Indian and Pacific Oceans
Length: 2.5m (8 ft)
Description: The stocky body is dark grey-blue on the upper side and pinkish white on the belly. Pale and dark stripes are prominent features running from the head lengthways along the flanks, and there are dark bands from the mouth to the insertion of the small flippers. The dorsal fin is also rather small. The beak is short and there are 34-44 sharply pointed teeth in each half of the upper and lower jaws.

General remarks: For a long time this dolphin was known only from a single carcass washed up on a beach in Sarawak, Malaysia, in 1895 but not described and identified until 1956. It was then known for some time only as a museum specimen. However, in the early 1970s the living animal was recognized in widely separated parts of the open oceans where it was identified in groups which could be made up of several hundred individuals. Not only are they a very gregarious species but they also mix frequently with other dolphins and whales. They are fast swimmers, charging to the surface to breathe, and while in some areas of the high seas they are reported to be shy of boats, at least off South Africa they will ride the bow wave. Their diet includes squid, crustaceans and fish, and this suggests that these dolphins are deep divers.

HARBOUR or COMMON PORPOISE

Phocoena phocoena

Family: Phocoenidae
Distribution: Coastal temperate and ice-free waters of the Northern Hemisphere
Length: 1.8m (6 ft)
Description: The chunky body has small flippers and the dorsal fin is usually low and triangular with a blunt tip. There is no beak, and there are 19-28 flattened spatulate teeth on each side of the upper and lower jaws. The pattern of colouring on the body is not sharply defined, with the dark brown-grey on the back shading down the flanks through paler grey to white on the underside.

General remarks: This little porpoise is generally found in harbours, estuaries and shallow coastal bays. Singles, pairs or groups of 5-10 are most often seen. They usually occur within the 100 fathom (183m) contour line of the shore and most often inside the 10 fathom (18m) depth range. They are active animals and fast moving, reaching speeds of up to 22km/h (14 mph). They are not always very conspicuous though, because they do not often approach boats. Many populations are permanent residents in particular localities, carrying out only limited inshore and offshore movements. They feed mainly on schooling fish such as herring, mackerel and sardines, as well as squid. A single calf is born at a length of about 75cm (2.5 ft) after a pregnancy lasting 11 months. Most births occur in the summer months and the interval between births is usually 1-2 years.

HECTOR'S DOLPHIN

Cephalorhynchus hectori

Family: Delphinidae
Distribution: Inshore shallow coastal waters around New Zealand
Length: 1.6m (5 ft)

Description: The body is dumpy in form, with a dorsal fin which is rounded and curves outwards at the trailing edge. There is no beak, and the mouth slopes up towards the eyes. The colouring is distinctive but complex, basically grey-black above, but with black on the sides of the head, flippers, dorsal fin and tail. The underside is white, with an extension up each flank, but a black band runs between the flippers. There are between 26 and 32 small teeth in each half jaw.

General remarks: This elegant-looking little dolphin usually forms groups consisting of 2-8 animals, although some larger numbers have been seen together occasionally. The species is restricted almost entirely to shallow waters that are no more than 80m (260 ft) in depth and within 8km (5 miles) of the coast of New Zealand, especially around the North Island and along the north-eastern coast of the South Island. They seem to be particularly attracted to the muddy water of river mouths and estuaries. They show rather little of their bodies when they surface to breathe, but they will ride the bow wave and follow in the wake of a ship. Their diet is varied and includes shellfish, crustaceans, squid and small fish, which are mostly taken on or near the sea floor. Calving takes place mainly in the spring and early summer months.

Family: Delphinidae
Distribution: The Indo-Pacific form, *S. chinensis*, occurs in coastal warm temperature and tropical waters of the Indian and West Pacific Oceans. The Atlantic form, *S. teuszii*, is found in similar waters off West Africa
Length: 2.8m (9 ft)
Description: The solidly built body is basically grey becoming paler below, and often speckled or spotted. There is a well-defined beak, with 29-36 teeth in the Indo-Pacific form and 26-31 teeth in each row in the Atlantic form. A distinctive hump provides a platform for the small dorsal fin in the mid-back, except in specimens found to the east of Indonesia.

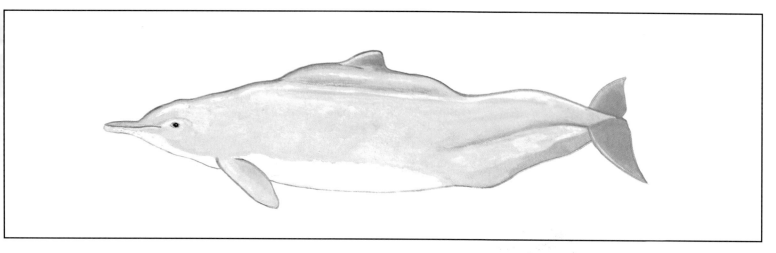

General remarks: There is quite a lot of variation in the colouring of the Indo-Pacific form. It may be that the animals with and without the hump, and to the west and east of Indonesia respectively, are separate species or sub-species. In the Indian Ocean the usual group size is six, though it can range from single animals to 12-20. There is considerable interchange between groups and little evidence of strong social bonds. They have been observed leaping clear of the water, waving a flipper in the air as they lie on their sides, and making body contact. They are frequently seen near bottlenose dolphins. Mating and births occur year-round but there is a peak of calving activity in summer. The main food taken is fish such as mullet. Off Mauritania the local fishermen beat the water to attract the Atlantic humpbacked and bottlenose dolphins which drive the mullet into their nets.

KILLER WHALE

Orcinus orca

Family: Delphinidae
Distribution: Found throughout the world, from the ice-floes to the tropics
Length: Males up to 9.5m (31 ft), females 7m (23 ft)
Description: The body is distinctively coloured. The back is shiny black with a grey saddle behind the dorsal fin. There is a white patch above and behind the eye, and white from the chin to the belly which extends up the flanks. The dorsal fin is particularly tall and erect in males, up to 1.8m (6 ft), but shorter and curved in females. The conical head has an indistinct beak, and there are 10-12 prominent teeth in each side of the jaws.

General remarks: Pods of 5-20 mixed males, females and young can remain stable over many years. Larger groups may form by the short-term joining together of several smaller pods. Some of these groups are resident in one area, others are migratory. Movements are often related to food availability and, in the polar seas, to ice cover. Pregnancy lasts for more than a year and the calves are usually born in the autumn at a length of 2.2m (7 ft). The young remain dependent for a prolonged period, so that the mother may not give birth again for 3-10 years. Killer whales are fast swimmers, reaching up to 45km/h (28 mph), and they frequently breach and 'spy-hop', when the broad paddle-shaped flippers are evident. They feed as top predators in the oceans, taking a wide range of fish, as well as birds, seals, dolphins and whales, in co-operative and organized hunts.

MELON-HEADED WHALE

Peponocephala electra

Family: Delphinidae
Distribution: Tropical and subtropical seas worldwide
Length: Females 2.7m (9 ft), males 2.6m (8.5 ft)
Description: This is a slender animal with a narrow tail stock. It is black or dark grey on the back, with slightly lighter colouring underneath and white lips. The head is rounded and tapers to a blunt point, with an indistinct beak. There are 21-26 small, sharply pointed teeth in each half of the upper and lower jaws. The high, curved dorsal fin is set midway along the body, and the flippers are long, slim and pointed.

General remarks: These whales form large groups of 150-1,500 animals, and they have been observed mixed together with Fraser's as well as spinner and spotted dolphins. They can swim very fast, and when frightened and in flight they typically form tight bunches, leaping and diving together in a flurry of foam. Mass strandings involving hundreds of specimens have been reported, but generally they live in the deep offshore waters of the equatorial zone. Their main food items are squid and a variety of small fish, but there are also reports of them attacking other smaller dolphins. Although little is known about their reproduction, newborn calves have been observed in spring (July-August) in the Southern Hemisphere, and near-term foetuses were also found in the pregnant females examined in a mass stranding at that time of year.

NARWHAL

Monodon monoceros

Family: Monodontidae
Distribution: The high Arctic
Length: 5m (16 ft) excluding the tusk, which can reach 3m (10 ft)
Description: The body is smooth and cylindrical with no back fin but a bumpy ridge along the rear mid-line. The small rounded head has a bulbous forehead, a crescent-shaped blowhole to the left of centre on top, and a small mouth. A straight spiralled tusk erupts through the left upper lip in the males. New-born calves are blotchy grey, juveniles bluish-black, the adults are mottled with white bellies; old animals are mostly white with dark spotting on the back.

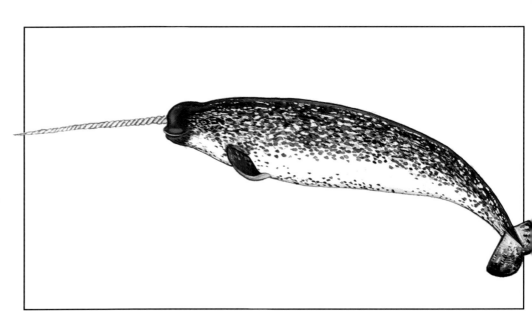

General remarks: Usually found close to and in the loose pack-ice, narwhals migrate in response to the seasonal movements of the ice cover. It is not uncommon for them to become trapped in the quickly-forming ice in the autumn. There is some segregation among the different classes, and groups of juveniles, females with calves and older males as well as mixed schools occur, normally not exceeding 10-20 individuals. Pregnancy lasts for 14-15 months and the calves are born in summer at a length of about 1.6m (5 ft). Lactation extends over a year and there is a three-year interval between births. Food includes squid, bottom fish, polar cod, crabs and shrimps. The large tusk of the males is probably a secondary sexual character used to establish a dominance hierarchy by sparring during the mating season in spring, giving rise to scarring on the heads of the adult males.

PILOT WHALES

Globicephala melas, G. macrorhynchus

Family: Delphinidae

Distribution: The long-finned species, *G. melas*, is found in cold temperate waters, the short-finned *G. macrorhynchus* in tropical and warm waters

Length: Long-finned males 6.2m (20 ft) and females 5.4m (18 ft). Short-finned males 5.4m (18 ft) and females 4m (13 ft)

Description: The sturdy black-grey body with a bulbous head has a prominent but low fin with a long base in the front half of the back. There are lighter markings on the throat and belly, and sometimes a pale saddle behind the dorsal fin. The flippers are about one-fifth of the body length in the long-finned species, but only one-sixth in the short-finned.

General remarks: Pilot whales travel in large herds, which can be composed of several hundred animals including all age and sex classes in the case of the long-finned species. The herds of the short-finned whale contain rather smaller numbers. Mass strandings of either species are not uncommon. The main food item for both pilot whales is squid, and the movements of the whales are probably governed by the behaviour of their prey, especially when the squid come inshore to spawn. Fish such as cod may also be eaten. The short-finned species tends to have fewer teeth, 7-9 in each row, than the long-finned whale with its 7-12. The short-finned species occupying the warm water tropical zones appears to breed year-round while the long-finned whales mate chiefly in spring and summer, giving birth 15-16 months later.

RIGHT WHALE DOLPHIN

Lissodelphis borealis

Family: Delphinidae
Distribution: The northern right whale dolphin is found in the temperate waters of the North Pacific Ocean
Length: Males 3.1m (10 ft), females 2.3m (7.5 ft)
Description: This is the only dolphin in the North Pacific which lacks a dorsal fin. The slender body is mainly black-brown with clearly demarcated white patches on the chin, throat and chest regions. This white marking extends as a band along the underside to the extremely narrow tailstock. The beak is small but distinct, and there are 36-49 sharply pointed teeth in each half of the upper and lower jaws.

General remarks: These are fast-swimming dolphins, reaching speeds of up to 40km/h (25 mph). They can leap gracefully from the surface of the water in a series of low bounds covering as much as 6m (20 ft) through the air at a time. In an alternative escape reaction they may scarcely break the surface to breathe, which with their smooth, finless backs makes them very difficult to detect even in calm sea conditions. They are gregarious animals, making up groups numbering hundreds or a few thousand individuals, and they are often found mixed with Pacific white-sided dolphins. Their major food items are squid and a variety of fish species. Seasonal shifts in distribution of the northern right whale dolphins to more southerly and inshore waters in the autumn, and northerly and offshore areas in spring, are probably related to the movements of these prey and to the water temperatures.

RISSO'S DOLPHIN

Grampus griseus

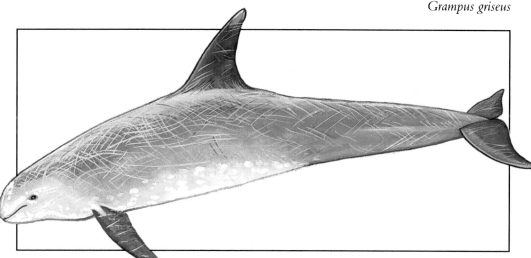

Family: Delphinidae
Distribution: Found in tropical and warm temperate deep seas worldwide
Length: 4m (13 ft)
Description: The thick-set body tapers towards the tail. It is white or light grey in adults, except for the tall, curved dorsal fin, the tail flukes and flippers, which retain the dark brown pigmentation of the juvenile. Extensive scratch marks and oval scars are common. The head is blunt with no beak, and there is a deep central furrow from the blowhole down the forehead. There are no functional teeth in the upper jaw and 14 peg-like teeth in the lower jaw.

General remarks: Although these dolphins are usually seen alone or in small groups of 12-25 animals, much larger aggregations have been observed as well. One interesting type of behaviour is for a group to swim in line with more or less even spacing between the individuals, presumably communicating to keep in formation. It is not uncommon to find them close to pilot whales, and they also mix with white-sided and right whale dolphins. The main food item in their diet is squid, for which they can dive deeply, and the hooks and suckers on the tentacles of this prey are the likely cause of the scarring which is so frequently seen on the dolphin's skin. Fish may also be taken occasionally. A friendly, large male Risso's dolphin nicknamed 'Pelorus Jack' regularly accompanied ships between Wellington and Nelson across the Pelorus Sound in New Zealand for 24 years at the beginning of this century.

SPINNER DOLPHIN

Stenella longirostris

Family: Delphinidae
Distribution: Tropical and sub-tropical waters around the world
Length: 2.2m (7 ft), females smaller
Description: The slender body varies considerably in shape and colour in different populations. The back is dark grey, but the underside may be pale or white, and more or less demarcated. The dorsal fin is erect and even appears to lean forward in males off Costa Rica, but curves back in the Hawaiian form. Adult males have a pronounced keel to the tail stock. The distinct slim beak has a black tip, and there are 45-65 sharp pointed teeth in each half of both jaws.

General remarks: This dolphin is named from its striking habit of leaping from the water and twisting a number of times in the air before landing again with a splash. Five different races are recognized: the Costa Rican is the longest, the eastern is the shortest, the northern and southern whitebelly forms are more sturdily built and like the Hawaiian form are whiter below. They all occur in large groups of 200-1,000 animals and are often found mixed with spotted and other oceanic dolphins. Pregnancy lasts for 10.5 months and a single calf is born at a length of about 80cm (2.5 ft). Females generally calve every 2-3 years. The main food items in their diet are schooling fish and squid. These dolphins are often found associated with yellowfin, and sometimes skipjack tuna so that fishermen locate the valuable fish below by the presence of the dolphins at the surface.

SPOTTED DOLPHIN

Stenella attenuata

Family: Delphinidae
Distribution: Found in the tropical and warm temperate waters of the Pacific, Indian and Atlantic Oceans
Length: 2.5m (8 ft)
Description: The coastal form is sturdier than the more slender offshore variety. The back is dark grey in colour, the belly paler, but the pattern varies in different localities. In all cases there is extensive but varied spotting. Older animals and those in the coastal populations have more spots. The dark dorsal fin is tall and curved, and the slender beak often has a white tip. There are 34-48 sharply pointed teeth in each half of each jaw.

General remarks: The number of species or races of spotted dolphins is in doubt. There is a range of colour as well as body characters in different populations, in addition to the distinctions between inshore and offshore forms in the Atlantic and Pacific Oceans. The numbers of dolphins in the coastal groups is generally from 50 to a few hundred, which is fewer than those found offshore, where large herds of a thousand or more animals are common. They mix with other oceanic dolphins, particularly spinner dolphins, and also associate with schools of yellowfin and skipjack tuna. Their main food items are surface-living fish and squid. They are very active animals, leaping high in the air and swimming vigorously. Mating and calving take place throughout the year, with pregnancy lasting just under twelve months. The calf is about 80cm (2.5 ft) long at birth and is unspotted.

STRIPED DOLPHIN

Stenella coeruleoalba

Family: Delphinidae

Distribution: Found in tropical and warm temperate waters worldwide

Length: 2.6m (8.5 ft)

Description: This is an elegant slim dolphin, blue-grey on the back, with a white belly. The flanks are grey with a variable pattern of two black stripes, one extending from around the region of the eye back to the flipper and the other towards the tail region. There is also a pale blaze crossing diagonally across the flank towards the tall curved dorsal fin. The beak is well defined and there are 45-60 sharp and slightly incurved teeth in each half of the upper and lower jaws.

General remarks: Herds of a few hundreds to several thousands of these highly social dolphins travel together in the warm, deep waters of the tropics. They are often segregated by age and sex, and large groups made up almost entirely of sexually immature animals are found with few if any mature males or females associated with them. Off Japan, where these dolphins have been studied most, there is an extended breeding season, with peaks in late summer, winter and spring. Pregnancy lasts for about 12 months and the single calf is 1m (3 ft) long at birth. It will stay with its mother for up to 3 years, but weaning is usually completed before this time. The main food is fish, squid and shrimps. These are acrobatic animals, able to leap 6-7m (20-23 ft) high and to perform a variety of twists and somersaults in the air, including backwards cartwheels.

Family: Platanistidae

Distribution: The Indus susu, *P. minor*, occurs in the Indus River, and the Ganges susu in the Ganges-Brahmaputra-Meghna river system of the Indian sub-continent

Length: Females 2.5m (8 ft), males 2m (6.5 ft)

Description: The plump grey-brown body has large, broad, almost rectangular flippers. There is a low, rather indistinct, hump or ridge instead of a dorsal fin. The long narrow beak is a distinctive feature, making up almost one-fifth of the body length. There are 27-33 sharply pointed teeth in each half of the jaws. The eyes are reduced to mere pinholes.

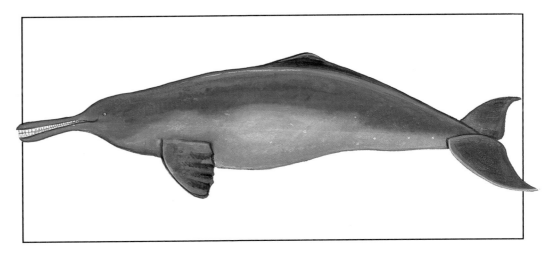

General remarks: The two species of susu are very similar to each other, differing only in their geographical distributions in the two major river systems, and some minor variations in the bones of the skull. The head is very mobile on the flexible neck. The eyes lack any lens, and as a result they are much reduced in function, although the animal may still be able to detect the direction and strength of any light. Susus swim on their left sides, nodding the head and emitting a stream of echo-location sounds which enable them to find their way about and to detect their prey in the muddy water conditions they inhabit. The main food items are fish and crustaceans. Pregnancy lasts about a year, and the single calf is born in spring at a length of 75cm (2.5 ft). Increased human use of the rivers and the construction of barrages are seriously affecting the chances of survival of these animals.

TUCUXI

Sotalia fluviatilis

Family: Delphinidae
Distribution: Inshore waters, rivers and estuaries along the northeast coast of South America from Brazil to Panama
Length: 1.9m (6 ft)

Description: The stubby body has an almost triangular dorsal fin. The forehead slopes down to a prominent beak, and there are 26-35 sharply pointed teeth on each side of the upper and lower jaws. The colour varies widely, depending on th location, which may be a sign that there more than one species. The back is gener ally dark – black, brown or grey – and th underside is pale grey or white.

General remarks: Groups of 2-25 of these little dolphins can be seen together, usually swimming in tight formation, which suggests that they have strong social ties. They are active swimmers, often leaping out of the water, and they are equally at home in the sea, brackish waters, and rivers. Those living in rivers may disperse during flood periods, but they generally tend to remain within a limited home range in the main river channels. The waters they inhabit are very turbid and muddy, and the repeated clicking sounds produced by the dolphins help them to find their way around by echo-location. Tucuxi in the Amazon river system give birth to a 70-80cm (2.5 ft) long calf from May to August after pregnancy lasting about ten months. Their chief food items includ fish, prawns and crabs, the actual species taken in different area probably depending on what is locally available.

WHITE-BEAKED DOLPHIN

Lagenorhynchus albirostris

Family: Delphinidae
Distribution: Found in the cold temperate and subarctic waters of the northern North Atlantic Ocean
Length: 3.1m (10 ft)
Description: The body is robust with a tall, curved dorsal fin, sharp-pointed flippers, and a short but distinct beak. The back and sides are dark grey-black and the underside is grey-white. The beak, as the common name suggests, is also grey-white, and there are two pale areas on each side of the body in front of and behind the position of the dorsal fin. There are 22-28 teeth on each side of both jaws.

General remarks: Large herds of up to 1,500 of these distinctively coloured dolphins have been seen, but the more usual group size is around 25 animals. They tend to be found in the northern part of their range during the summer months, and to be distributed further south in the winter, but the migrations are poorly understood. Mating and births are thought to occur chiefly between June and September. The newborn calf is about 1.2m (4 ft) in length. In Newfoundland these dolphins are known as 'squidhounds', and in addition to their main food of squid, the diet includes octopus, as well as fish such as cod, capelin and herring, and sometimes bottom-living crustaceans. They do not come to ships or bow-ride, but they will breach clear of the water. It is not uncommon for single, older animals to strand.

WHITE-SIDED DOLPHIN

Lagenorhynchus obliquidens

Family: Delphinidae
Distribution: The Pacific white-sided dolphin occurs in the cooler northern parts of the North Pacific Ocean
Length: 2.3m (7.5 ft)
Description: The tall dorsal fin is sharply hooked backwards, dark in colour on the leading edge and paler towards the rear. The back of the body is black, with a pair of white or light grey stripes running from the head to the tail stock. The flanks are grey, and separated from the whiter belly by a black stripe. The dark beak is short and thick, and there are 23-32 sharply pointed and slightly curved teeth in each half of the jaws.

General remarks: This is a very gregarious dolphin, usually foun in groups of up to 200 but sometimes forming huge her numbering several thousands of animals of all ages and sexes mixe together. They also associate with other dolphin species, particular common and northern right whale dolphins, as well as sea birds ar California sea lions. They are vigorous swimmers, often leapir clear of the water, and they will ride ships' bow waves. Althoug some populations are resident in certain areas, seasonal shifts distribution have been noted in others. These move northward summer and southward in winter, and sometimes they mal inshore and offshore movements associated with changes in wat temperatures. Most calves are born in summer at a length of 8(95cm (2.5-3 ft). Squid, anchovies and hake are the chief items the White-Sided Dolphin's diet.